Elvis
and the Scooter

Maoliosa Kelly
Illustrated by Martin and Ann Chatterton

Elvis got a new scooter.

"I want to go out," said Elvis.
"Where can I go?"

He went up.

He went down.

He went round and round.

4

"Now I want to go fast,"
said Elvis.

The scooter went fast.

"Help! I can't stop!" said Elvis.

9

Elvis zoomed out into space.
"Help!" said Elvis.

Elvis was lost.

"Where am I?" he said.

"I want to go home."

The scooter zoomed
down, down, down.
It went fast.

"Where is Elvis?"
said Mum.